DREAM
POCKET BOOK OF
COLOURING

Parragon

Bath • New York • Cologne • Melbourne • Delhi
Hong Kong • Shenzhen • Singapore

This edition published by Parragon Books Ltd in 2016

Parragon Books Ltd
Chartist House
15–17 Trim Street
Bath BA1 1HA, UK
www.parragon.com

Images are courtesy of Shutterstock and iStock
Cover design by Beth Kalynka

ISBN 978-1-4748-4129-0

Printed in China

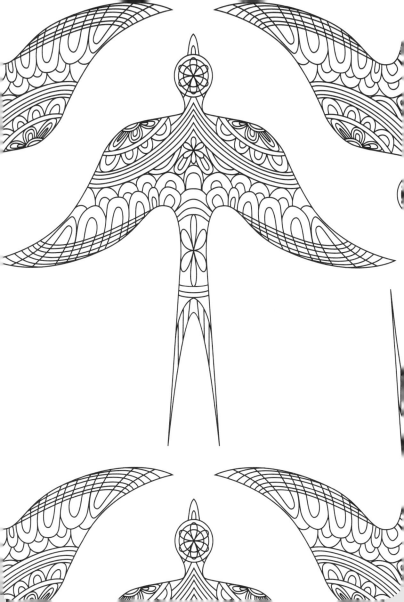